JOSEPH,

Jacob's Favorite Son

Genesis 37, 39, 41, 44–46 for Children
Written by Eric C. Bohnet
Illustrated by Gina Capaldi

CONCORDIA PUBLISHING HOUSE • SAINT LOUIS

I'm Joseph, an Egyptian prince;
Well, that's what I am now.
But I was born a Hebrew boy;
To the true God I bow.

My father, Jacob, had twelve sons;
Ten were older than me.
But father always liked me best.
This caused some jealousy.

He gave me a terrific coat,
So colorful and bright,
With red and yellow, purple too.
It was a pretty sight.

My brothers did not like me much,
Especially when I dreamed.
I dreamed that they'd bow down to me.
How proud I must have seemed!

One day, they threw me in a pit
And sold me as a slave!
Far off to Egypt I was dragged.
At least my life was saved.

In Egypt, things got even worse
When I was thrown in jail.
But God was always there with me.
His love would never fail.

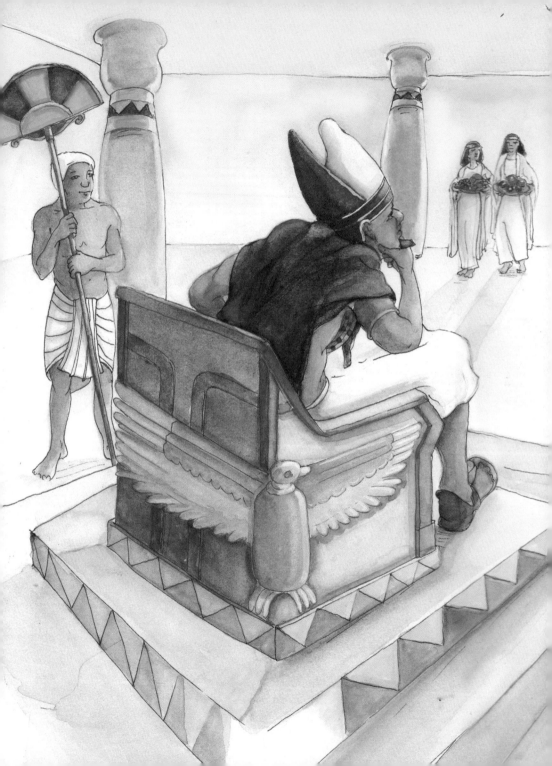

One day, the Pharaoh
   had a dream
Of fat and skinny cows.
He heard I could interpret it,
And God had shown me how.

The dream warned Pharaoh
   there would be
A famine in his land.
I told him he should save up food.
He put me in command.

One day, my brothers came to buy
The grain that I had stored.
They did not recognize me dressed
As an Egyptian lord.

I didn't tell them who I was;
I tried to test them first.
Would they protect young Benjamin?
I still did fear the worst.

This time, they did their father's will.
"Take all of us," they cried.
"Let Benjamin return to Dad.
We'll stay here at your side."

No more could I disguise myself!
Instead, I wept and cried,
"I am your brother Joseph! Is
My father still alive?"

They all were stunned to hear this news
And quite afraid of me.
But quickly I forgave their sin:
"God had a plan, you see."

I told them there'd be five more years
Before the rain would fall.
"But here I can take care of you,
Our family, one and all."

But God still had much bigger plans
For Jacob's family.
From us He'd later send His Son
To save both you and me.

Just like my brothers, we sin too,
And need to be forgiven.
It's for our sins Christ Jesus died,
So we may enter heaven.

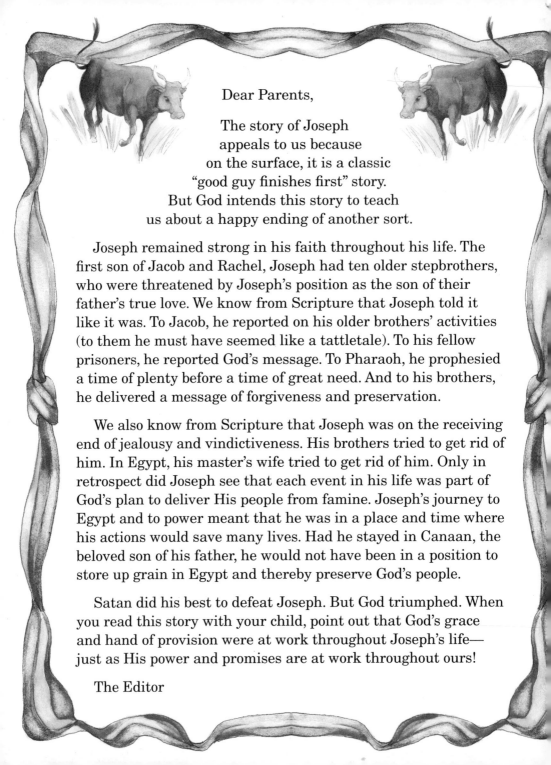

Dear Parents,

The story of Joseph
appeals to us because
on the surface, it is a classic
"good guy finishes first" story.
But God intends this story to teach
us about a happy ending of another sort.

Joseph remained strong in his faith throughout his life. The first son of Jacob and Rachel, Joseph had ten older stepbrothers, who were threatened by Joseph's position as the son of their father's true love. We know from Scripture that Joseph told it like it was. To Jacob, he reported on his older brothers' activities (to them he must have seemed like a tattletale). To his fellow prisoners, he reported God's message. To Pharaoh, he prophesied a time of plenty before a time of great need. And to his brothers, he delivered a message of forgiveness and preservation.

We also know from Scripture that Joseph was on the receiving end of jealousy and vindictiveness. His brothers tried to get rid of him. In Egypt, his master's wife tried to get rid of him. Only in retrospect did Joseph see that each event in his life was part of God's plan to deliver His people from famine. Joseph's journey to Egypt and to power meant that he was in a place and time where his actions would save many lives. Had he stayed in Canaan, the beloved son of his father, he would not have been in a position to store up grain in Egypt and thereby preserve God's people.

Satan did his best to defeat Joseph. But God triumphed. When you read this story with your child, point out that God's grace and hand of provision were at work throughout Joseph's life— just as His power and promises are at work throughout ours!

The Editor